The Good Samaritan

Written by Sasha Morton
Illustrated by Cherie Zamazing

Jesus was preaching the word of God to his followers one day, when a man asked him, "Teacher, what must I do to make sure I get to heaven?"

Jesus replied, "You must love God with all your heart, and love your neighbour as you would love yourself."

Then, Jesus told everyone this story.

3

A Jewish man was walking down the long,
steep road from Jerusalem to Jericho.

The path was winding and rocky,
yet this was not the reason everyone
feared travelling down this path.

It was feared for the many twists and turns
in the road, which meant it was easy for robbers
to lie in wait to steal from people.

Unfortunately, that was exactly what happened to this particular man.

He was making his way down the hill when a band of robbers jumped out in front of him and stole his money, and everything he was carrying. They beat him so badly he fell to the ground and could not move.

There the man lay, sure that he was close to death. He would only survive if someone came by and helped him.

After some time had passed,
the man heard someone coming
down the hill. He would be saved!

He called out for help…

But the approaching person – a priest –
did not stop to help. He took one look at
the injured man and crossed over to the
other side of the road.

Sadly, the man closed
his eyes and waited for
death to take him.

Then he heard someone else coming down the hill. He would be saved!

He called out for help…

11

But once again, the approaching person
– a preacher – crossed over to the other
side of the road.

Despairingly, the
beaten man closed his
eyes once more.

After a while, he heard someone
else coming down the hill.
Surely this time he would be saved?

But when he looked up, he saw
that this traveller was a Samaritan.
Because Jewish people did not get
along with Samaritan people, the
man believed there was no chance
that this traveller would stop.

13

But this Samaritan did not see a Jew, he just
saw a man in pain who needed his help.

Gently, the Samaritan
helped the beaten man
to sit up.

He spoke kindly to him.
Then, he gave the man
something to drink,

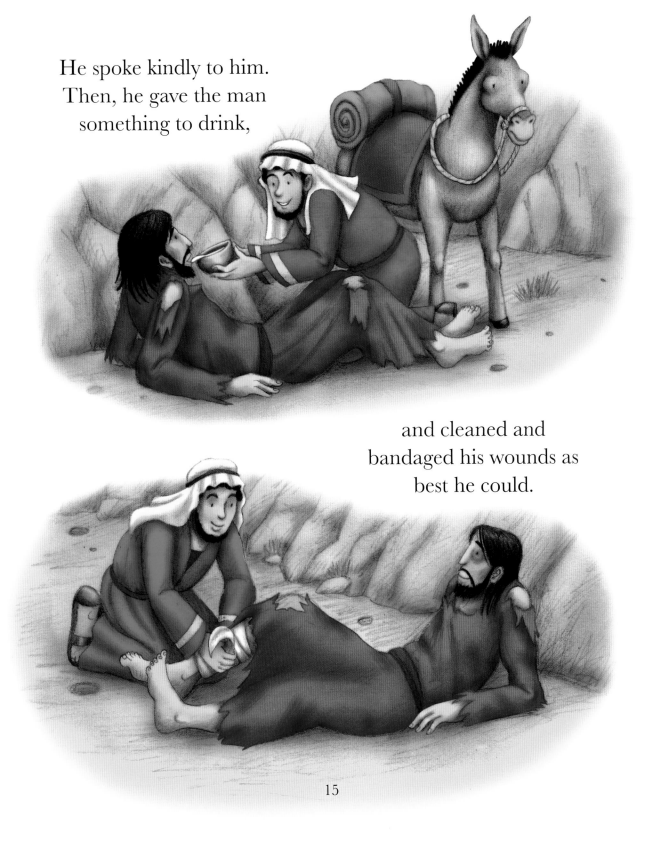

and cleaned and
bandaged his wounds as
best he could.

Carefully, the Samaritan helped the man on
to the back of his own donkey and they slowly
continued their journey into Jericho.

The man was very grateful to
this stranger – the only person
who had helped him.

The Samaritan took the man
to an inn where he himself
was staying. That night,
he cared for the man and made
sure he was comfortable.

Before he went on his way the next morning,
the Samaritan spoke with the innkeeper.

"Please look after
this man while I am
gone," he said.

With that, he gave the innkeeper some of his own money and told him, "Take these coins, and on my way back I will repay you for any extra expense his stay here may cost you."

The innkeeper gladly did so and with his help the man
recovered, thanks to the good Samaritan.

When he had finished telling this tale, Jesus asked his followers,
"Which of these three, do you think, was a good
neighbour to the man who was robbed?"

22

"The one who took pity on him," answered one of the men.

Jesus replied, "Go, and do the same yourself."

For God wants his children to look after everyone around them, no matter who they are.

23

An Hachette UK Company
www.hachette.co.uk

First published in Great Britain in 2014 by Ticktock,
an imprint of Octopus Publishing Group Ltd
Endeavour House
189 Shaftesbury Avenue
London
WC2H 8JY
www.octopusbooks.co.uk
www.ticktockbooks.co.uk

ISBN 978 1 84898 934 4

A CIP record for this book is available from the British Library.

Printed and bound in China

10 9 8 7 6 5 4 3 2 1

With thanks to Jana Burson

Series Editor: Lucy Cuthew Design: Advocate Art
Publisher: Tim Cook Managing Editor: Karen Rigden
Production Controller: Sarah-Jayne Johnson